SCHOOL BUS OF HORRORS

DESTRUCTION ZONE

BY MICHAEL DAHL

ILLUSTRATED BY EUAN COOK

raintree
a Capstone company — publishers for children

Raintree is an imprint of Capstone Global Library Limited, a company incorporated in England and Wales having its registered office at 264 Banbury Road, Oxford, OX2 7DY – Registered company number: 6695582

www.raintree.co.uk
myorders@raintree.co.uk

Designed by Bob Lentz
Original illustrations © Capstone Global Library Limited 2019
Design element: Cover background by Shutterstock/Evannovostro
Production by Tori Abraham
Originated by Capstone Global Library Ltd
Printed and bound in India

ISBN 978 1 4747 5930 4
22 21 20 19 18
10 9 8 7 6 5 4 3 2 1

British Library Cataloguing in Publication Data
A full catalogue record for this book is available from the British Library.

CONTENTS

From dawn to dusk, the **SCHOOL BUS OF HORRORS** rumbles along city streets and down country roads, searching for another passenger. Yellow, black markings, dirty windows – it looks like any other school bus.

But **BEWARE!** Step aboard this bus and

experience the scariest ride of your life . . .

CHAPTER ONE
DEAD THINGS

"Who cares about a museum?" says Ivy.

She shakes her head, tossing her long braided hair.

"Especially a *doll* museum," she adds. "Talk about creepy!"

Ivy is standing in the queue to get on a bus.

Today is Field Trip Day.

"Hurry up, everyone," says her teacher, Mr Hong. "We'll be leaving in five minutes."

Ivy rolls her eyes. "Boring."

Her friend Gracie chews her gum. "Totally," she agrees.

Ivy steps onto the bus.

She is surprised that she can't see the driver.

The shadow of a man sits behind a plastic wall.

His voice comes through a few small holes in the barrier.

"I agree with you girls," says his whispery voice. "Who wants to see a lot of dolls?"

Ivy and Gracie rush down the narrow aisle and quickly find a seat.

"Creepy," says Ivy.

"You said it!" says Gracie.

"Should we tell Mr Hong?" asks Ivy.

A rumbling sound comes from under the floor.

The bus lurches forward.

Gracie looks around.

"He's not here," she says. "Maybe he's on the other bus."

CHAPTER TWO
THE CRASH

The bus zooms down the street. It strikes a dustbin on the kerb.

Ivy holds on to her seat and glances out of the window.

"He's going too fast!" she says.

Other kids around her start shouting.

A boy sitting at the front of the bus screams.

The driver steps on the brakes.

SCREEEEECH!

The bus turns sideways, skidding down the street.

Ivy and Gracie are thrown from their seat.

"Look out!" screams a boy.

"We're going to hit that building!" shouts Gracie.

CHAPTER THREE
THE WRONG LANE

The strange bus zooms down the street.

Ivy looks out of the window.

"The driver is going pretty fast," she says.

"That's no good," Gracie says. "I'm not in a hurry to get to that stupid museum."

Ivy remembers what the bus driver said. *Dolls. Who wants to see a lot of dolls?*

The bus picks up speed.

"Excuse me, driver!" says Mr Hong.

That's weird, thinks Ivy. *I thought*
Mr Hong was on the other bus.

"We just passed the museum!"
Mr Hong shouts.

Gracie points at the windscreen.

"We're in the wrong lane!" she screams.

The driver steps on the brakes.

The bus turns sideways, skidding down the street.

The boy in the front seat screams.

The windscreen shatters.

CHAPTER FOUR
THE SAME LORRY

The bus zooms down the street.

Ivy turns in her seat and looks out of the dirty window.

"It certainly is taking a long time to get there," she says.

"Hey!" says a boy at the front.
"The museum is back there!"

Gracie stands up in her seat.

"He's right," she says.

BRRRUMMMMMPP!

The children fly out of their seats.

Ivy's braids smack against
her face.

"Excuse me, driver," says
Mr Hong. "I think we just passed
the museum!"

An icy fist grips Ivy's stomach.

"This has happened before," she
says aloud.

Gracie looks at her. "What did you say?"

"This has all happened before," Ivy replies. "We passed the doll museum a little while ago."

Gracie stops chewing her gum.

"But we've just got here," she says.

"No," says Ivy. "We were here before!"

"Before?" says Gracie. "What do you mean?"

The bus swerves wildly down
the street.

HONKKK! HONNNNK!

A big lorry rushes past the bus
windows.

"That lorry!" says Ivy. "I've seen
that lorry before."

"Ivy, you're freaking me out!" says
Gracie.

The driver steps on the brakes.

The bus turns sideways, skidding down the street.

The bus slams into a building.

The windows on both sides of the
bus crack and shatter.

It's OK, Ivy tells herself. *This has all happened before.*

Ivy looks towards the front.

She can see the plastic wall. But she can't see the driver's shadow sitting behind it.

Suddenly she can't see anything.

How can we be in a tunnel? she thinks. *The bus isn't moving!*

The bus zooms down the street.

All the bus' windows are back in place. The cracks have disappeared.

Ivy's throat dries up. She can hardly speak.

"Gracie," she croaks.

Ivy turns to her friend.

A life-sized doll, shaped like Gracie, sits next to her.

Gracie's eyes are just painted on.

Ivy stands up and screams.
"Mr Hong! Mr Hong!"

Mr Hong is slumped in his seat.
His eyes are also painted on.

None of the people surrounding
Ivy are real.

Ivy screams again as the top of
the bus flies off.

A dark shadow fills the bus.

And a gigantic hand reaches down towards her.

"It's my turn," says a boy. "I get to crash the bus this time."

"You never do it right," says a girl.

The boy hands his friend a small doll with bright braids.

"Put this one back in the box," he says. "She's not fun anymore."

GLOSSARY

aisle walkway that runs between the rows of seats on a bus

barrier wall that prevents people or other things from going past it

creepy unpleasant or frightening

glance look at something very quickly

lurch move in an unsteady, jerky way

museum place where interesting objects are displayed

swerve change direction quickly, usually to avoid something

DISCUSS

1. Why do you think this book is called *Destruction Zone*?

2. At the end of the story, the passengers have turned into dolls. Do the illustrations in this book provide any clues to this conclusion? Explain.

3. What's the scariest bus journey you've ever experienced? What made it so terrifying?

WRITE

1. Create a new title for this book. Then write a paragraph on why you chose your new title.

2. Write a story about a scary field trip!

3. Write your own School Bus of Horrors story. Who will the bus pick up next?

AUTHOR

MICHAEL DAHL is the author of the Library of Doom series, the Dragonblood books and Michael Dahl's Really Scary Stories. (He wants everyone to know that last title was not his idea.) He was born a few minutes after midnight of April Fool's Day in a thunderstorm, has survived various tornados and hurricanes, as well as an attack from a rampant bunny at night ("It reared up at me!"). He currently lives in a haunted house and once saw a ghost in his high school. He will never travel on a school bus. These stories will explain why.

ILLUSTRATOR

EUAN COOK is an illustrator from London, who enjoys drawing pictures for books and watching foxes and jays out of his window. He also likes walking around looking at broken brickwork, sooty statues and the weird drainpipes and stuff you can find behind old run-down buildings.

SCHOOL BUS OF HORRORS

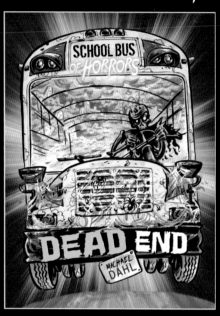